© 1992 Susan Higson
Published exclusively for
Safeway
6 Millington Road, Hayes, Middx UB3 4AY
by Julia MacRae Books
a division of Random House
20 Vauxhall Bridge Road
London SW1V 2SA

First published 1992

Printed in Hong Kong
ISBN 1-85681-264-2

Godfrey's Birthday

Susan Higson

SAFEWAY SUPERBOOKS

Today is Godfrey's birthday!

Will anyone remember?

Time to get
dressed, Godfrey!

Birthday breakfast
time, Godfrey!

Who's at the door,
Godfrey?

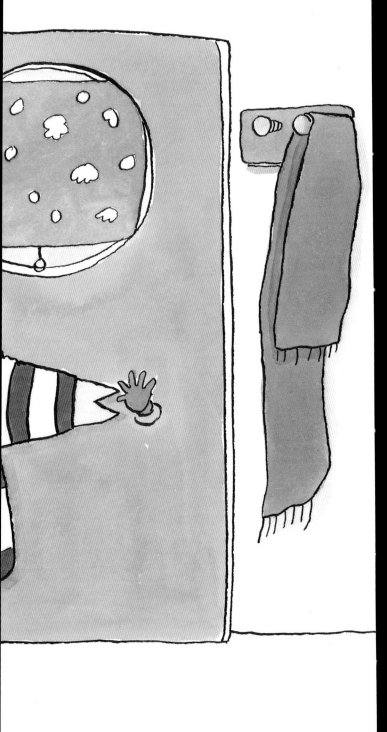

Who left the parcel, Godfrey?

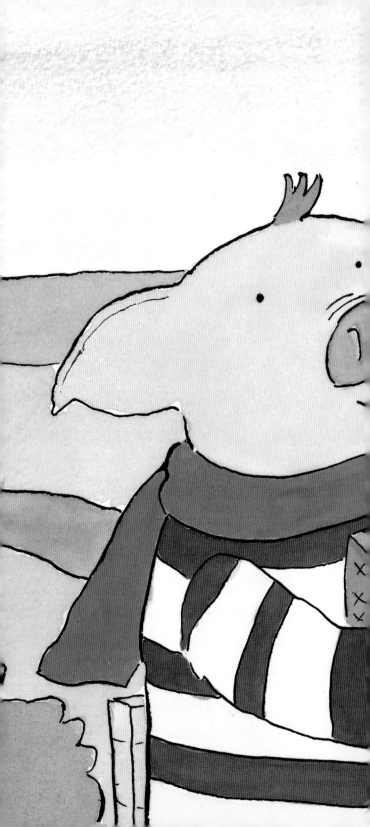

Knock on the door,
Godfrey!

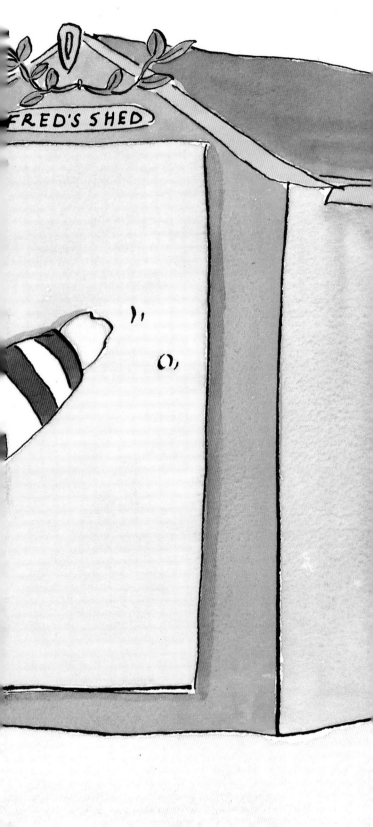